AFTER

MW00773578

BIPOLAR HEAL THYSELF!

Troy Steven

Foreword by Dr. Beth Ann Mahoney, DO

Battle Press
SATELLITE BEACH, FLORIDA

AFTER YOUR BIPOLAR DISORDER
Bipolar Heal Thyself!

The information, ideas, and suggestions in this book are not intended as a substitute for professional advice. Before following any suggestions contained in this book, you should consult your personal psychiatrist or mental health professional.

Battle Press books may be ordered through booksellers or by contacting:

Battle Press
1-919-218-4039
steve@battlepress.media
www.battlepress.media

ISBN: 979-8-9854-2994-7 (softcover)
ISBN: 979-8-9854-2995-4 (eBook)

Library of Congress Control Number: 2022905640

First Edition

Personal Information

Enter your personal information
here:

Name: _____

Address:

_____

_____

Phone #: _____

Emergency Contacts:

Name: _____

Phone #: _____

Name: _____

Phone #: _____

Health Care Professional:

Name: _____

Phone #: _____

CONTENTS

DEDICATION

I dedicate this book
to all of you Bipolar Warriors
Fighting the War against
Bipolar Disorder.

Live by the Motto:

Bipolar Heal Thyself!

THANKS

The author wishes to sincerely thank my Psychiatrist, Dr. Beth Ann Mahoney, who wrote the Foreword for this book and continues to help me manage bipolar disorder successfully.

A special thanks to my friends:

David Ferrier, who continues to inspire and mentor me in my publishing endeavors, and

John Mandala, who provided the template for this book.

FOREWORD

It is my pleasure to write this Foreword. I find this book educational for patients who are newly diagnosed, or have been coping with bipolar disorder for years, and wanting to change the course of their life. This book is well organized in a concise style outlining how to better understand and avoid the road to destruction. I cannot emphasize enough the need to understand what is happening to you or a loved one.

This book gives you suggestions on how to find a psychiatrist and work with them. There are many good concepts on learning how to give feedback on your medications and the danger of stopping taking them and ending up back to square one. Talk Therapy will help you to learn positive ways to think, process your life and learn to live a better life. Troy talks of the benefits of online and DBSA support groups for peer support. Learn about mood diaries and good books that may also help. You'll need to become your own best advocate.

This is a well thought out endeavor by this author, who has battled bipolar disorder for over 25 years. Having gone the long road Troy wants to help others avoid the pitfalls he had to endure.

Dr. Beth Ann Mahoney, DO

If you find this book useful, please take a few moments to write a short review. Your help in spreading the word is highly valued and reviews make it much easier for readers to find the book. Thanks!
Troy Steven

https://www.amazon.com/dp/B0BCD5C7BL#customerReviews

A NOTE FROM TROY

This is a book I wish I had when I was diagnosed with bipolar disorder in 1993. I could have avoided a lot of pain and suffering if I knew what I know now.

My hope is that through the use of this book men and women fighting the war against bipolar disorder will gain the expertise and proficiency to successfully manage this devastating and sometimes life-threatening illness.

I am giving you a call to arms to become a bipolar warrior. Fight, claw, and scratch with all of your strength, courage, and willpower to overcome the bipolar beast that invades your mind and wants to destroy you. This is the most difficult and important undertaking you will ever face! No one deserves a negative kind of life, and I am passionate in my belief that it should not happen to you or to anyone else.

Most importantly, never give up, have faith in yourself and the universe, and make your dreams come true! It is in your power.

YOU'VE GOT THIS!

INTRODUCTION

"I think it's completely reasonable to feel like you're unwilling to face your diagnosis in the beginning. What's important is that you keep trying, day by day."
—**Mariah Carey**
One of the most successful singers and songwriters of all time with eighteen number 1 hits and more than 200 million records sold.
(Diagnosed with bipolar disorder)

Bipolar disorder is a condition that cannot be ignored or underestimated. The implications are simply too serious: suicide or living a crippled, limited life, reckless or violent behavior, financial problems, personal and professional relationships undermined, loss of self-respect, and sometimes most tragically, giving up on your dreams.

The first step is accepting that you aren't alone. Consider this list of many notable individuals who have survived and thrived with symptoms of bipolar disorder: Demi Lovato; Mariah Carey; Mel Gibson; Russell Brand; Bebe Rexha; Halsey; Ted Turner; Jim Carrey; Frank Sinatra; Catherine Zeta Jones; Winston Churchill; Selena Gomez; Jean-Claude Van Damme; Harrison Ford; Vincent Van Gogh; Abraham Lincoln; Kanye West; Kristy McNichol; Marilyn Monroe; Florence Nightingale; Brooke Shields; Ben Stiller; and Owen Wilson.

Remember that these are only some of the people who are brave enough to admit that they have bipolar disorder or are known to have coped with symptoms of bipolar disorder. Millions suffer daily. Struggling alone, oftentimes afraid to confess to others or confront their condition, too many go unnoticed and untreated until it's too late.

Unfortunately, I must include myself in this list. I have bipolar disorder, having struggled since 1993 and am all too aware of what it takes

11

to confront and battle this illness. I have survived three major episodes, which have resulted in three separate visits to psychiatric hospitals, one due to a suicide attempt. All the while, I obtained a Master's degree, maintained a career as an Aerospace Engineer for over 20 years, and currently own my own book publishing company. I am also the proud parent of four awesome kids and blessed with three grandchildren. This goes far beyond me, though.

The idea of creating a Bipolar Battle Plan began after I attempted suicide in 2007. I almost succeeded. Afterward, I promised myself I would do anything and everything I could to keep it from happening again. I realized I had to make major changes in the way I was managing the illness, in my treatment plan, and in the way I was living my life.

> *"The definition of insanity is doing the same thing over and over again and expecting different results."*
> —**Albert Einstein**

AFTER YOUR BIPOLAR DISORDER

With hopes to help others, I have had to confront my darkest thoughts and demons to write this book, which has not been easy. I actually attempted to take my own life. Today I have found balance and achieved security by creating a battle plan to overcome bipolar illness. I have successfully used the plan over time to remain episode free and advance toward achieving my dreams.

Useful Tips:

1. This book is not simply to read, it is meant to be *used*. There are checklists and room to take notes that will be invaluable to review as time passes. Begin to use this book *now*, as a planner, reminder, and data source.

2. Always remember there are Help Lines with people on call at all times. Some examples include:

- Suicide & Crisis Lifeline
  Call or text (988) or call (1-800-273-8255)
- Mental Health Hot Line (1-844-549-4266)

- Substance Abuse and Mental Health Help-line (1-800-662-4357)
- Crisis Text Line (Text 'HOME' to 741741)
- Most importantly, if you are in trouble and your life is on the line, dial 911

3. Most of you have a cell phone, tablet, or computer. There are some good Apps available to help you manage bipolar disorder – see Appendix A for some examples.

NOTES:

CHAPTER 1:
CREATE YOUR BIPOLAR BATTLE PLAN

"Without victory, there is no survival."
—Winston Churchill
41st British Prime Minister
(Believed to have had bipolar disorder)

How do we battle a mental illness that has the ability to take control of our thoughts and emotions and cause our minds to deceive and betray us? How do we overcome an illness that has the power to cause us to attempt suicide, become violent, and spend money recklessly, not to mention act in so many other destructive ways? How do we surmount the health issues attributed to bipolar disorder such as a shorter life span, obesity, diabetes, and abuse of drugs and alcohol?

The best solution is to follow a lifelong Battle Plan based on the expert recommendations of the medical community.

> **The consensus is that successful treatment of Bipolar Disorder depends on diligently following a comprehensive treatment plan, including:**
> - *Educating yourself about the illness*
> - *Medication*
> - *Communicating with your psychiatrist and therapist*
> - *Having a strong support system*
> - *Helping yourself by making healthy lifestyle choices*

This chapter guides you through the process of creating your personal bipolar battle plan. First, you will establish your goals and objectives (reasons to fight), next you will be presented with a toolkit of nine powerful tools that will help you win the war against bipolar disorder. Then you will learn how to train yourself to be a bipolar warrior.

I don't claim to be an expert. I make decisions based on whether I am experiencing bipolar symptoms, the state of my mental and physical health, financial well-being, status of my relationships with my significant other, children, family, and friends, and level of satisfaction with my career. If changes are needed, I adjust my battle plan. Each of you will have different circumstances and challenges than I do, so you should tailor your battle plan accordingly.

> *"Our goals can only be reached through the vehicle of a plan, in which we must fervently believe and upon which we must vigorously act. There is no other route to success."*
> -Vincent van Gogh
> (Believed to have lived with Bipolar Disorder)

Establish Your Goals and Objectives

The first rule of combat is to believe in your reasons to fight, which are your goals and objectives. This is the key: you must believe that you WILL win. Not that it will happen, but that it should happen and that you are in charge.

When establishing your goals and objectives, consider your deepest wants and desires, your dreams, and what you want to achieve before leaving this great earth. Don't limit yourself—you deserve the best of everything!

Consider the following questions when setting your goals and objectives:

1. What motivates me?
2. What interests me?
3. What would I do more of if I could?
4. What do I care about?
5. Where do I want my life to go?
6. What brings me joy?
7. What are my dreams and desires?

The goals and objectives I set for my bipolar battle plan include:

1. Effectively deal with any bipolar symptoms or side effects that may occur.
2. Eliminate bipolar episodes.
3. Never again attempt suicide.
4. Maintain strong mental and physical health.
5. Establish lasting financial security.
6. Be in a romantic relationship with an intelligent, desirable woman who enjoys my company as much as I enjoy hers.
7. Continue to enjoy and foster good relationships with my kids, extended family, and friends.
8. Laugh out loud on a regular basis.

Bipolar Battle Plan Toolkit

For those of us who have bipolar disorder, it is important to understand that we are facing a highly complex situation and can't hope to change it until we arm ourselves with the necessary psychological and intellectual capacity.

The tools you select to include in your bipolar battle plan can be thought of as techniques, tactics, and knowledge you can deploy as needed to battle the enemy, bipolar disorder.

BIPOLAR BATTLE PLAN TOOLKIT

Tool 1: Contingency (Emergency) Plan (Chapter 2)

The Contingency Plan is one of the most important tools to master in the overall battle plan. The purpose of the Contingency Plan is to keep you alive, out of the hospital, and out of jail when you are having a bipolar episode. It is the last line of defense to keep a manic episode from skyrocketing out of control or a depressive episode from plummeting to disaster.

Tool 2: Enemy Recon (Chapter 3)

The more knowledge and understanding you have of bipolar disorder, the better you can control your illness. It is important to educate yourself on all aspects of bipolar disorder, just like you would do if you were going to have a major operation such as brain surgery or kidney replacement. Study the subject like you are getting a College Degree in Bipolar Disorder. Never stop learning!

Tool 3: Optimize Your Medication
(Chapter 4)

Learning how to determine the best medications to treat your bipolar illness is imperative and can be one of your most powerful tools in fighting the war against bipolar disorder. Your psychiatrist will prescribe your medications, but you are the only one who can tell if they are working effectively. You must become an expert at finding the medications and corresponding dosages that work best for you.

Tool 4: Find the Right Psychiatrist
(Chapter 5)

Finding a psychiatrist who you trust to treat your bipolar disease and keep you healthy, alive, and out of the hospital is essential. The skills, abilities, and competence of your psychiatrist to repair, tune up, and maintain your mind can be likened to that of an auto mechanic who is the only person you trust to work on your car.

Tool 5: Train Your Mind
(Chapter 6)

Your mind is your most powerful ally. Your thoughts are the only thing over which you can exert complete control. What you think and believe becomes a reality and rules your life. However, for those of us who have bipolar disorder, it is a paradox that we must use our mind to fight a disease that at times has the power to take control of it. This chapter includes powerful techniques for training your mind.

Tool 6: Train Your Body
(Chapter 7)

If you take care of your body, your body will in turn take care of you. Your mind and body are a unit; being good to your body benefits your mind. Taking care of your body will help stabilize your mood and maximize your energy for the battles ahead.

Tool 7: Recovering from a
Bipolar Episode
(Chapter 8)

By definition, a bipolar episode never ends well, unacceptable things have happened, your mind has deceived you, and you crashed and burned. Now you are left to pick up the pieces, regain your balance, and try to get back on an even keel. Chapter 8 offers tactics and strategies that can speed up your recovery.

Tool 8: Psychiatric Hospitals
(Chapter 9)

Hopefully, you will never have to spend time in a psychiatric hospital. However, if you do, knowing what to expect is invaluable in speeding up your recovery and shortening your hospital stay.

Tool 9: Legal Rights
(Chapter 10)

If you have bipolar disorder there are certain legal issues that may arise related to your condition, including job discrimination, consent to treatment issues, and trouble with the law.

Bipolar Warrior Training:

> *"There is no such thing as tough; there's trained and there's untrained."*
> **—Denzel Washington**
> **(Man on Fire)**

The next step is to begin you training and master the fundamental technical and tactical skills necessary for warfare. This includes conditioning your mind and body. Conditioning is not only used for the purpose of conditioning for something, but it is also used for the purpose of conditioning against something.

> *The Only Reason a Warrior Lives is to Fight, and the Only Reason a Warrior Fights is to Win.*

A Warrior:

- Knows that this is a battle for their life.
- Understands the will to conquer is the first condition of victory.
- Never accepts the unacceptable.
- Makes a plan to defeat the enemy.
- Knows that no plan survives first contact with the enemy.
- Knows that wars are won on strategy, not impulse.
- Knows that until they understand exactly what is going on and how to stop it, the most important tool in their arsenal is reason.

TROY STEVEN

- Has Faith in themselves and the universe.
- Remains calm and in control at all times.
- Knows that every minute lost in war can be the cause of defeat.
- Makes up their mind to overcome struggles and challenges.
- Adopts the mindset of a warrior every morning when they wake up.
- Always does their best.
- Prepares to battle.
- Knows they are at war with the parasite in their mind.
- Fights with all their might.
- Takes action to further their plan on a daily basis.
- Focuses on what they can control.
- Knows that once they face down the enemy, they are able to accommodate, or even work with them.
- Rolls with the punches.
- Knows their strengths and weaknesses.
- Avoids being taken by surprise.
- Knows that even a badass needs rescued every once in a while.
- Practices vigilance.

- Learns as much as possible because information is power.
- Voices and directs daily intentions.
- Respects their enemies.
- Knows that sometimes they have to change things up.
- Trains their mind and body.
- Shores up their defenses wherever needed.
- Eats healthy and stays hydrated.
- Never gives up.

NOTES:

CHAPTER 2:
CONTINGENCY (EMERGENCY) PLAN

"A wise man once told me to always have a Contingency Plan."
—Abraham Lincoln
16th President of the United States
(Believed to have lived with bipolar disorder)

The Contingency (Emergency) Plan is one of the most important tool to master in the overall Battle Plan. The purpose of the Contingency Plan is to keep you alive, out of the hospital, and out of jail when you are having a bipolar episode.

Take a second to comprehend the following statistic about suicide and bipolar disorder:

> **Statistics show that up to 20 percent of people with bipolar disorder end their life by suicide, and 20-60 percent of us attempts suicide at least once in our lifetime.**
> **(Dome, 2019)**

Are you kidding me? One in five of us kills ourselves. **Un-freaking believable!**

In my experience, there is a point in time during either a manic or depressive episode when I have a lucid moment and realize I need to seek help. This is the critical point in time when I must launch my Contingency Plan. It is the point of no return, if I do nothing, things always end badly.

An important part of my Contingency Plan is the prearranged agreement I made with my psychiatrist regarding what to do if I start going off the deep end during a bipolar episode. There have been times during a bipolar episode, or while recovering from an episode, where I suddenly go from being fine to feeling like swallowing all my medications, jumping off a bridge while taking a walk, or running at top speed through a grocery store because I feel like I am going to explode. It is as if a switch has been thrown and my brain has been invaded by a crazy man who has hijacked my thoughts.

When this happens, I have to fight with all my might to avoid disaster. When I talked this over with my psychiatrist, he told me to carry a 400 mg tablet of Seroquel (one of my medications) in my pocket and take it immediately if I start having these feelings, even if I have to chew it.

Another critical part of my Contingency Plan was to assemble a team of people who I can call for help when my bipolar illness starts to get the best of me. My team consists of my psychiatrist, my daughter Rachel, and my Uncle Bud. They all know my history and struggles with bipolar disorder, and I trust them with my life.

My Contingency Plan is as follows. Tailor it and make it your own. Use the form on the next couple of pages and put it in writing.

If I am having a Bipolar Episode, I will do the following:

- Ensure I am getting sufficient sleep. If not, I will call my doctor and request a sleep aid.
- Call my psychiatrist and make an appointment to see her ASAP or talk to her on the phone.
- Adjust my medication dosage(s) per the pre-arranged plan I made with my psychiatrist.
- Call the people I recruited to be part of my Contingency Plan.
- Distance myself from my loved ones if I feel agitated, violent, or out of control so they are safe.
- Check myself into the hospital if things get bad enough.
- Remove myself from stressful situations.
- Start taking my medications if I am not currently taking them.
- Stop drinking alcohol and doing drugs.

- Exercise and get fresh air every day.
- Stay hydrated.
- Take vitamins and eat healthy.

NOTES:

YOUR PERSONAL CONTINGENCY PLAN

My Contact Information:
Name: _____
Phone: _____
Address:
_____

My Doctor's Contact Information:
Doctor's Name: _____
Phone Number: _____
Address:
_____

If my Doctor is not available, contact these medical professionals:
_____
_____
_____

Support Team: Name   Phone Number
Support Person 1:
_____
Support Person 2:
_____

Support Person 3:
_____

Current Medications:
_____
_____
_____

Medication Contingency Plan:
_____
_____
_____

Allergies To (Intolerance of any Medication):
_____
_____
_____

Things That May Trigger a Relapse:
_____
_____
_____

Mania Early Warning Signs:
_____
_____
_____

Depression Early Warning Signs:

_____
_____
_____

Warning Signs That a Crisis May be Developing:

_____
_____
_____

Things Your Support Team Can Say That Are Calming and Reassuring:

_____
_____
_____

What is Most Important to Me and Worth Living For:

_____
_____
_____

I Have a Psychiatric Advance Directive:
YES: _____   NO: _____

If "YES" Attach it or Note Where it Can be Located:
If "NO" One Should Be Created in Case of Emergency.

Signature:

_____

Date:

_____

*Remember to Make a Few Copies of Your Contingency Plan and Give Them to the People in Your Support Team.

24-Hour Emergency Numbers:
1) Immediate Emergency   Call 911
2) Suicide & Crisis Lifeline
     Call or Text (988) or call 1-800-273-8255
3) Mental Health Hotline   1-844-549-4266
4) Substance Abuse and Mental Health Helpline
                    1-800-662-4357
5) Crisis Text Line   Text 'HOME' to 741741

A PLAN IS USELESS IF NOT PUT INTO ACTION!

CHAPTER 3:
ENEMY RECON

"Bipolar depression really got my life off track. But today I'm proud to say I'm living proof that someone can live, love and be well with bipolar disorder when they get the education, support and treatment that they need."
—**Demi Lovato**,
American Singer/Pop Star
(Diagnosed with bipolar disorder)

Bipolar disorder is a very complex illness. It's also very serious and life-threatening. The more you know about bipolar disorder and how it affects you, the better you can manage and overcome the illness.

It is important to educate yourself on all aspects of bipolar disorder, just like you would do if you were going to have a major operation such as brain surgery or kidney replacement. Study the subject like you are getting a College Degree in bipolar disorder. Never stop learning.

What is Bipolar Disorder?

Bipolar Disorders are described in the American Psychiatric Association's Diagnostic and Statistical Manual of Mental Disorders (DSM-5) as a group of brain disorders that cause extreme fluctuation in a person's mood, thoughts, energy, and ability to function (Truschel, 2020).

Bipolar disorder is also known as manic depression because a person's mood can alternate between the "poles" - mania (highs) and depression (lows). The change in mood can last for hours days weeks or months. Not everyone's symptoms are the same, and the severity of mania and depression can vary.

Bipolar disorder can affect a person's energy level, judgment, memory, sleep patterns, sex drive, and self-esteem. It has also been linked to anxiety, substance abuse, and health problems such as diabetes, heart disease, migraines, and high blood pressure. You may be asking yourself: *"What doesn't bipolar disorder affect?"*

People with bipolar disorder may go for long stretches of time without symptoms. However, the condition is usually cyclical, so be prepared for it to worsen and then improve at times. For those of us who live with bipolar disorder, this means accepting that mood swings and episodes of mania or depression will always be a potential challenge for us.

As you become familiar with your illness, you can learn your own unique patterns of behavior. If you learn to recognize these signs and seek effective and timely care, you can often prevent additional episodes. Recognizing and naming your typical bipolar symptoms is the first important step to understanding and beginning to take control over your bipolar disease.

The typical symptoms I have when I am experiencing a bipolar episode include:

AFTER YOUR BIPOLAR DISORDER

- Heightened Awareness – Feeling like Superman
- Impulsiveness
- Hallucinations that someone is out to get me
- Energy Fluctuations in my mood - highs and lows
- Grandiosity
- Believe I am talking to God directly

Make a list of your typical bipolar symptoms:

_____

_____

_____

_____

What Bipolar Is Not

Bipolar disorder is not a character flaw or sign of personal weakness.

Bipolar Disorder Facts & Statistics

Here are some startling facts and statistics that show how dangerous and deadly bipolar disorder can be:

- Up to 20 percent of people with bipolar disorder end their life by suicide, and 20-60 percent of them attempt suicide at least once in their lifetime (Dome, 2019).
- More than 40 percent of people with bipolar disorder struggle with alcohol and drug abuse (Cerullo, 2007).
- Bipolar disorder affects approximately 5.7 million American adults, or about 2.6 percent of the US population age eighteen and older in a given year (Kessler, 2005).
- Bipolar disorder results in 9.2 years reduction in expected life span (National Institute of Mental Health, 2019).
- People with bipolar disorder are three times more likely to develop diabetes than members of the general population (Thompson, 2010).

- Three of the top methods of bipolar suicide are guns, suffocation (hanging), and poisoning (overdose) (Mariant, 2012).
- Approximately 15 percent of people with bipolar disorder have had a violent episode. (Vann, 2010).
- Bipolar disorder doesn't discriminate by age, race, ethnicity, or social class. It affects as many men as women (Sachs, 2008).
- There are many factors leading to medication non-adherence in psychiatric patients, including lack of insight into having an illness, distress associated with side effects affecting quality of life, lack of family and social support, insufficient information on the disease and treatment, and substance abuse or addiction (Mert, 2015).
- There are no specific blood tests or brain scans to diagnose bipolar disorder (Krans, 2015).

Three Types of Bipolar Disorder

Bipolar Disorders are a category described by the American Psychiatric Association's Diagnostic and Statistical Manual of

Mental Disorders (DSM-5) that includes three different conditions: Bipolar I, Bipolar II, and Cyclothymic Disorder. These 3 conditions are used to diagnose people with the illness and determine treatment plans accordingly (Truschel, 2020).

Bipolar I Disorder (Mania or a Mixed Episode): Bipolar I Disorder is the classic manic-depressive form of the illness. It is characterized by one or more manic episodes that last at least a week or require hospitalization. The person may also experience a major depressive episode that lasts 2 weeks or more. Some mood episodes may have mixed features (symptoms of both depression and mania). Bipolar I Disorder can exist both with and without psychotic episodes.

Bipolar II Disorder (Hypomania and Depression): Bipolar II Disorder consists of depressive and manic episodes which alternate and do not inhibit function. The mania is typically less severe than in bipolar I, and doctors call it hypomania. A person with Bipolar II may experience a major depressive episode preceding or following a manic episode.

Cyclothymic Disorder:
This type is a cyclic disorder that causes brief episodes of hypomania and depression. These symptoms do not fit the criteria for wholly manic or depressive episodes.

Note From Dr. Beth Ann Mahoney, DO on Diagnosing Bipolar Disorder

"Some people are not diagnosed properly. If they see a doctor who only has 1 hour to diagnose and treat (say in a rehab) it's not a true diagnosis. You can't come to solid conclusions in one visit! Sometimes they were on a mind-altering substance so the ups and downs of patients self-medicating can paint a picture of 2 poles.

Then there are patients who have borderline personality disorder and diagnose themselves bipolar as it's more vogue. Ask those people if they are on medical marijuana or any substances. They couldn't be diagnosed clinically!

One of the criteria for being diagnosed with bipolar disorder is that it's in the absence of Substances (including alcohol and marijuana) during reported symptoms of mood disorder. It used to be a year off substances to have a firm diagnosis. I have also had patients say they have only depression because they want an antidepressant to get them the high of euphoria. Of course, their prognosis is poor. The more cycling causes more dysfunction in daily living and increases the difficulty of managing the illness and more medication to keep a good baseline."

How Common is Bipolar Disorder in Children?

Because bipolar disorder tends to run in families, having a parent with bipolar increases the likelihood that a child also will develop bipolar. When one parent has bipolar disorder, the risk to each child is estimated to be 15 to 30%. When both parents have the disorder, the risk increases to 50 to 75% (bp Magazine, Summer, 2022).

Symptoms of mood disorders may be difficult to recognize in children and adolescents because they can be mistaken for age-appropriate emotions and behaviors or overlap with symptoms of other conditions such as attention-deficit/hyperactivity disorder (ADHD). However, depression and anxiety in children may be precursors to bipolar and should be carefully evaluated and monitored.

Bipolar Episode Triggers

For each of us, our stressors and triggers are different. Identifying the triggers that may set you off can help you to avoid a bipolar episode. Once you identify your personal triggers, you can work on recognizing them as they occur and handle them more effectively. Bipolar triggers may include:

_____ Sleep irregularities

_____ Increase in stress

_____ Financial problems

_____ Isolation

_____ Stopping taking medications or forgetting to take them

_____ Alcohol and/or drug abuse

_____ Side effects from medications

_____ Change of seasons

_____ Conflict with others

_____ New relationships
_____ Lack of exercise
_____ Travel and jet lag
_____ Birth of a child
_____ Feelings of loneliness and despair
_____ Non-supportive family or friends
_____ Relationship problems and breakups
_____ Change in sleeping habits
_____ A death in the family
_____ Stress at work
_____ Promotion at work
_____ A vacation
_____ Change in environment
_____ Moving residences
_____ Poor nutrition
_____ Physical illness
_____ Loss of employment
_____ Taking on more than you can handle
_____ Changing jobs
_____ Thyroid malfunction

Sleep Disturbances

Getting sufficient sleep is **CRUCIAL** if you have bipolar disorder. Sleep disturbances are a key symptom of both mania and depression and an excellent early warning sign of a mood change. Your ability to get a good night's rest is highly influenced by the circadian system, which is the body's twenty-four-hour internal biological clock. The circadian rhythm of your body determines when you need sleep, and when you need to wake. It is through this rhythm that your body knows when to start and stop certain chemicals in your brain. To put it simply, regulated sleep stabilizes the brain chemicals that control emotions. Maintaining a consistent sleep schedule and wake time can help you avoid nighttime sleeplessness or daytime exhaustion, which can increase the risk of new episodes of mania or depression.

When you go to sleep easily, sleep and dream deeply, and then wake up refreshed on a set schedule every day, you're experiencing regulated sleep. Things that can keep you from getting sufficient sleep include:

_____ Shift work or work that upsets your sleep patterns such as an ever-changing schedule
_____ Stress
_____ Drugs and alcohol
_____ Caffeine

____ Travel to different time zones
____ Anything new: baby, job, city, etc.
____ Frisky bed partner (might be worth losing some sleep ☺)
____ Bright light before bed

Mania Warning Signs

If you are experiencing a manic episode, remember this rule of thumb: "What goes up must come down." Mania causes people with bipolar illness to climb higher and higher and then crash like a wave rolling into the shore.

Use the following checklist to determine if you are experiencing manic symptoms:

____ Similar pattern of symptoms from previous episodes
____ Extremely irritable mood, agitation, feeling jumpy or wired
____ Grandiose delusions and hallucinations, such as a direct connection to God
____ Increased sex drive
____ Being easily distracted
____ Increasing goal-oriented activities, such as starting new projects or businesses

AFTER YOUR BIPOLAR DISORDER

_____ Having an unrealistic belief in one's abilities

_____ Behaving impulsively

_____ Reckless behaviors, such as spending sprees, impulsive sex, risky business investments

_____ Heightened mood, exaggerated optimism overvalued self-confidence

_____ Inflated sense of self-importance, feeling bullet proof

_____ Increased physical and mental activity and energy

_____ Paranoia or hallucinations

_____ Racing speech and thoughts

_____ Argumentative, picking fights

_____ Jumping from one thought to another or project to project

---

Depression Warning Signs

When most people think of bipolar disorder, they think of the manic side. However, depression is the far more common and more damaging of the two poles. In the euphoria of mania, people rarely choose to intentionally harm them-

51

selves. In a deep depression, however, self-mutilation and suicidal thoughts and actions are far too common.

Use the following checklist to determine if you are experiencing depressive symptoms:

_____ Similar pattern of symptoms from previous episodes

_____ Suicidal thoughts

_____ Sleep disturbances

_____ Abandoning activities you usually enjoy

_____ Continually having negative thoughts

_____ Changes in appetite

_____ Prolonged sadness or unexplained crying spells

_____ Loss of energy

_____ Increased feelings of worry and anxiety

_____ Social withdrawal and isolation

_____ Feelings of guilt or hopelessness

_____ Little interest in sex

_____ Inability to concentrate or make decisions

_____ Unexplained aches or pains

_____ Slowed and difficulty thinking

_____ Paranoia, hallucinations

_____ Self-Loathing

CHAPTER 4:
OPTIMIZE YOUR MEDICATION

"When you ramp up, it expresses your personality more. You can become almost adolescent in your expression. When you don't take medication every day to keep you at a certain state, you have the potential to ramp up - and even end up in the hospital."
—**Kayne West**
American Rapper
(Diagnosed with bipolar disorder)

This chapter explains how to determine the best medications and corresponding dosages to effectively battle your bipolar illness and achieve optimal mental and physical health.

Caveat: Some people with bipolar disorder can manage the illness without medication. If so, just be sure you are satisfied with how your life is going: are you mentally stable? Are you happy? Are you living your best life?

Note From Dr. Beth Ann Mahoney, DO About Medication

I decided to dig a little deeper to get more insight and asked my psychiatrist Dr. Mahoney about her experiences. She responded as follows:

"Yes, I have had patients who don't take medication, but they don't do well. I just heard that one of my patients I have been seeing for a while completed suicide. She refused to accept this diagnosis and she went from alcohol to Crack and drove her car into a tree at a high speed. She left 2 children without a mother. I also had a patient with bipolar disorder when I was a resident and we'd stabilize her and she'd get discharged, then come back 2 weeks later

very psychotic off all her medications. She eventually ended up decompensating looking more like a schizophrenic and stopped going back to baseline.

Each story is different. They just tell you they aren't on medications...but are they? I can't save everyone with bipolar disorder. You need intelligence and therefore want to improve your life. Not every person with a "bipolar" diagnosis has bipolar disorder and medications help stabilize but you can lead a horse to water, but you can't make them drink!"

Accept You Need to Take Medication

Like heart disease or diabetes, bipolar disorder is a biological illness and most often, medication is required to treat it. Medication can bring your mania and depression under control and prevent relapses once your mood has stabilized. Bipolar disorder has several different symptoms, reflecting difficulties in several different areas or systems of the brain. Different medicines target separate brain functions. You may need medicines to help stabilize your mood, curb manic symptoms, relieve depressive symptoms, help you sleep, manage anxiety, control psychosis, improve information processing, or compensate for side effects.

People with bipolar disorder are often reluctant to admit there is a problem. It takes most of us more than one bipolar episode before we are convinced that we have a mental illness. The more pain, agony, and disruption to our lives that is caused by a bipolar episode, the sooner we become *Believers*. It is a landmark event when you accept that you have bipolar disorder and need to take medication to treat your illness.

When you accept that medicine is necessary to minimize symptoms and avoid future episodes, you can reallocate the energy you have been expending rejecting the medicine and channel it into finding the medications that work best.

You must be your own judge and jury to determine whether you need to take medication—no one else is in a fitting position to do so. Make the decision based on the ramifications of having another bipolar episode, and optimizing your health, happiness, and life. You may also want to consider whether trying medications to treat your illness could additionally benefit those around you—the people you love and care for. Sometimes we are apt to make positive life changes when considering others rather than ourselves.

Research Your Medications

The first step to optimize your medication is to educate yourself on each medication you are taking, or thinking about taking, by using internet research, reading books, and collaborating with your psychiatrist. Then answer the following questions:

1. How will I know if the medicine is working?
2. What are the expected results or pros of the medicine?
3. What are the side effects and risks or cons of the medicine?
4. What is the target dosage and therapeutic range for this medication?
5. What time of day should I take the medicine?

6. Are there any foods or other substances I will need to avoid?
7. How will this drug interact with my other prescriptions?

Become Your Own "Mental Detector"

Next, train yourself to become your own "Mental Detector" by monitoring your thoughts, moods, and energy levels on a regular basis. Ask yourself the following questions:

1. Have I laughed today?
2. Do I feel like myself?
3. Am I looking forward to something coming up in the future?
4. Did I barely drag through the day?
5. Do I have a good libido?
6. Am I having any psychotic thoughts?
7. Am I possibly displaying depressive or manic behaviors? If so, how can I best explain to my psychiatrist or to a loved one how my behaviors are 'out of the norm?'

Dialing-In Your Medications

Dialing-in your medications to the optimal dosage is one of the most valuable skills to master. This is where the rubber meets the road. Most bipolar individuals take more than one medicine at a time and determining the "medication cocktail" that works best takes time, patience, and skill. It's important to work closely with your psychiatrist and reevaluate your medication regularly, because the perfect dosage may change over time.

In addition, you need to become skillful at rating your medications and determining if they are working or not. It is very helpful to have a methodology to use to determine if your medicine is dialed-in to the optimum dosage. Answer these questions to rate how well your medications are working:

1. Are you sleeping well?
2. Are your moods generally positive?
3. Does the medicine provide benefits? If so, what are they?

4. Do you have any bipolar symptoms? If symptoms persist, do they seem different or downplayed in any way?
5. How is your energy level?
6. Are you experiencing any side effects?
7. Are you being sociable?
8. Do you feel good physically?
9. Are you thinking clearly and logically?
10. What does your heart and intuition tell you?
11. Do you have sexual awareness and drive?
12. Do you feel stable?
13. Do you feel angry?
14. Do you feel like a robot?
15. Are you overly anxious?
16. Are you depressed?
17. Are you manic?

It takes skill, finesse, and guts galore to determine the specific medications and dosages that will effectively combat your bipolar disorder. Just as it takes time and practice to learn golf or a new language, learning how to use the powerful pharmaceutical medications to effectively treat your bipolar illness is a skill that improves with experience.

> **It is your job to push the limits of your medications to find the sweet spot where you are mentally sharp and focused; have plenty of get up and go; a positive attitude; no bipolar symptoms; and are happy with yourself and your life.**

Unfortunately, this process is far from easy. It would be awesome if the first time you are prescribed medication to treat your bipolar illness, the medicine(s) worked wonderfully, suppressed your symptoms, and kept you from having future bipolar episodes. However, this is rarely the case, and it is more likely that adjustments will need to be made to your medications as time goes on. Do not be afraid to take calculated risks in making changes with buy-in from your psychiatrist.

> **You do not want medications to make you feel mediocre; you want them to make you feel great!**

Substitute Medicine for Alcohol and Drugs

An important statistic to keep in mind is that more than 40 percent of bipolar individuals abuse alcohol or drugs (Cerullo, 2007). For many of us, it is an attempt to self-medicate. Instead of seeking health care, we use drugs or alcohol to mask uncomfortable feelings. There's a cultural bias that makes us think, "I should be able to fix this myself, so I'll use the chemicals that I have available to me to help do that."

The fact of the matter is that you are using depressants to treat your disease. Numbing or masking bipolar symptoms will only make things worse.

Do not underestimate the negative effects of alcohol and drugs on your mind and body. Why abuse illegal drugs and alcohol when you have some of the strongest pharmaceutical drugs at your disposal? Take the responsibility to not abuse alcohol or drugs.

Useful Tips:

1. It can be extremely detrimental to stop taking your medications, especially all at the same time. Two of my bipolar episodes escalated out of control when I stopped taking my medications when I became manic. The first time I flushed them down the toilet, and the second time I threw them into a field. I ended up in the psychiatric hospital on both occasions.

2. Keep a close eye on your medications and don't let yourself run out or forget them if you go on a trip. It is easy to do and has happened to me more than once. Going without my medications for even a couple of days will drastically mess with my mind. Also, I keep an extra set of daily medications in my vehicle in case I forget to take my pills in the morning.

3. If you don't have prescription insurance coverage, or even if you do, there are huge savings to be had by using GoodRx (www.goodrx.com). For example, I filled a prescription for 30 days of 400 mg tab-

lets of Seroquel. Since I don't have prescription insurance it was going to cost $370. Fortunately, using GoodRx, it only cost me $17 for the same prescription.

NOTES:

CHAPTER 5:
FIND THE RIGHT PSYCHIATRIST

"No pill can help me deal with the problem of not wanting to take pills; likewise, no amount of psychotherapy alone can prevent my manias and depressions. I need both."
—Kay Jamison
Writer, Professor of Psychiatry
(Diagnosed with bipolar disorder)

Finding a psychiatrist who you trust to treat your bipolar disease and keep you healthy, alive, and out of the hospital is essential. The skills, abilities, and competence of your psychiatrist to repair, tune up, and maintain your mind can be likened to that of an auto mechanic who is the only person you trust to work on your car.

Choosing a psychiatrist is no easy feat because someone else's "good" may not be "good" for you. Everyone is different. The best course of action is to research and interview a doctor—just like hiring an employee to work for you. While "good" is different for each person, one thing remains the same: a good psychiatrist is one with whom you are happy. That's all. A good psychiatrist is one who performs to your expectations, whatever those may be.

Trust is by far the most important aspect to consider when choosing a psychiatrist. You are putting your trust in this person with your emotional and mental well-being. One of the most important roles of your psychiatrist is for them or their staff to be available anytime, day or night, in your time of crisis. If you recognize you need help because of your bipolar illness, contact your psychiatrist immediately. Don't put it off until later for any reason. If a receptionist answers your phone call, tell them in no uncertain terms that you need to talk to your psychiatrist as soon as possible. If it is outside of office hours, call the psychiatrist who is on-call—that is what they are there for.

Rating a Psychiatrist

Remember, you are the customer paying a professional for their services. If your current psychiatrist isn't meeting your expectations, find someone who is better suited for your needs.

Here is a list of criteria that will help you find the right psychiatrist to treat your bipolar illness:

- They establish a Contingency Plan with you and tell you to call day or night if you need help.
- They give you instructions on how to modify your medication in the event of serious bipolar symptoms.

- They are skillful at determining your state of mind and zeroing in on your current problems.
- You feel like you can trust them.
- You value their advice.
- They are easy to talk to, and make you feel comfortable.
- They have several years of experience treating bipolar disorder.
- They have hands-on experience in psychiatric hospitals.
- They promote a whole-life wellness plan.
- They are very knowledgeable about medication.
- They explain the pros and cons of each medicine, including possible side effects.
- They explain how to ramp up each medication to the therapeutic range.
- They are covered by your insurance.
- They won't put up with bullshit.
- They are knowledgeable about new research and methods for treating bipolar disorder.
- They are board certified.
- They answer your questions without judgement.

Getting the Most Out of Appointments

Prior to having an appointment with your psychiatrist, it is smart to prepare in advance what you plan to discuss and accomplish. When the appointment begins, your psychiatrist will try to gauge how you are doing and your state of mind. If you are manic, depressed, experiencing noticeable bipolar symptoms, or side-effects, tell your doctor. Keeping your true thoughts or feelings a secret from your doctor will only harm you in the long run.

Keep a Journal or Mood Chart

Keeping a journal or mood chart and sharing it with your doctor is a great way to explain what has been going on with you since your last appointment, especially if you aren't satisfied with the medications you are currently taking.

A mood chart is a monthly diary that tracks your illness, treatment, and other factors to help you better manage bipolar disorder. Charting your moods may reveal a pattern behind the highs and lows of bipolar disorder, such as a change in medication, dosage or some other factor that might otherwise have gone unnoticed. Over time, a mood chart may serve as an early warning radar to help predict when depressive or manic phases may begin. Stressful occurrences or a change in sleep patterns that precede the start of the depressive cycle can be identified, and steps taken to help you. Filling out your chart takes only a few minutes each day, and it can go a long way to help you and your doctor manage bipolar disorder.

You can find example mood charts on the internet. One example is found at:
https://www.therapistaid.com/worksheets/bipolar-mood-log

The Perfect Medication Cocktail

PARTNER WITH YOUR PSYCHIATRIST TO FIND THE PERFECT MEDICATION COCKTAIL

After questioning you about your mood and state of mind, your psychiatrist will ascertain what dosage you are taking of each of your medications. Then they will assess your medication regimen and decide, based on your input, whether to make a change in the dosage of one of your current medications, or counsel you whether to stop taking a medication or to start taking a new one. Before the appointment, decide whether your current medicine regimen is optimizing your potential, or you feel that a change is needed. If the medicine is not working, be prepared to state the reasons why. Keeping a log or journal is very helpful. The more specific you can be, the better your doctor can treat your condition. If you feel strongly that you need a change in your medications, then stick to your guns.

The doctor prescribes medication for you and then will make modifications based upon your feedback. It is your responsibility to keep making changes to your medications until you find the perfect medication cocktail for optimum mental and physical health. It's your life, your brain, and your happiness that are at stake. Keep working with your psychiatrist to find the medications that make you whole.

Finding a New Psychiatrist

Helpful pointers for finding a new psychiatrist include:

- If you have insurance and want to stay in-network, call your insurance company for a list of names. You may be able to look at reviews from other patients if you search in-network providers online.
- If you know someone who likes their doctor, try to schedule an appointment with that same doctor.
- Call your state psychiatric society and ask for a referral.
- Ask your primary care doctor. They are used to making referrals.
- Ask any psychiatrist. They tend to know one another. If you can get one on the phone, they may give you names without seeing you in person.
- If you're a student, try the school's counseling or health center. The staff may also be able to suggest off-campus referrals.
- Search online and pick a few out of the heap and research them.

Once you find a potential psychiatrist call and make an appointment. For your first appointment, you need to decide what questions to ask the doctor to find out if they are a good fit for you. During the first meeting, the doctor is going to be interviewing you. But remember that you are the client and should be interviewing them as well.

The questions you ask are about opening a dialogue on issues that matter to you. It's not about judgment as much as it is about exploration. You're testing the waters to see if this is the person you think is most able to help you. Do not be intimidated by them whatsoever just because they are doctors.

Here is a list of questions you may want to ask:

1. How long have you been practicing as a psychiatrist?
2. What percentage of your patients have bipolar disorder?
3. What happens if I have an emergency outside of office hours?
4. Have you ever worked in a psychiatric ward or hospital?

5. How do you decide what medications and dosages to prescribe for your patients?
6. What is your view on psychotherapy?
7. How often do you typically see your patients?
8. How long are appointments?
9. How much does an appointment cost?
10. What is your typical treatment plan for your bipolar patients?
11. What is your view on supplements and alternative medication?
12. Are there any medical conditions that could be causing or exacerbating my mood swings?

It is okay if a doctor doesn't meet your expectations. Not every doctor is for every person, and there's nothing necessarily wrong with either of you. If it doesn't work, it doesn't work. It is like a first date. First dates don't always lead to second dates. If you decide it is not going to be a good match, now is the easiest time to say something simple like, "I don't think we're the best therapeutic match. Can you please provide a referral to someone else?"

Ultimately, at the end of the day it is your life, and who you hire to be your psychiatrist is your choice. Your psychiatrist works for you. They are your employee, and you pay them for their services. You decide whether to hire or fire them.

Psychotherapy

Besides prescribing medication, some psychiatrists provide psychotherapy. If they don't, they can usually refer you to a therapist. Therapy can help people reduce stress levels, regulate moods, and change thinking patterns that may trigger episodes. Also, research has established that using psychotherapy in combination with medication to treat bipolar disorder further reduces both the number of relapses that people experience as well as the severity of those relapses. One of the most important outcomes of therapy is self-awareness. For a person with bipolar disorder, self-awareness may mean realizing different events that are likely to trigger a relapse and learning to recognize signs and symptoms of the onset of depression or mania.

In her book *Touched with Fire*, Kay Jamison talks about the benefits of psychotherapy:

"Psychotherapy, in conjunction with medication, is often essential to healing as well as the prevention of possible recurrences. Drug therapy, which is primary, frees most patients from the severe disruptions of manic and depressive episodes. Psychotherapy can help individuals come to terms with the repercussions of past episodes, take the medications that are necessary to prevent recurrence, and better understand and deal with the often-devastating psychological implications and consequences of having manic-depressive illness." (Jamison 1994).

How Therapy Can Help

Therapy can help you:

- Understand your illness.
- Overcome fears or insecurities.
- Cope with stress.
- Make sense of past traumatic experiences.
- Separate your true personality from the mood swings caused by your illness.

- Identify triggers that may worsen your symptoms.
- Improve relationships with family and friends.
- Establish a stable, dependable routine.
- Develop a plan for coping with crisis.
- Understand why things bother you and what you can do to alleviate these issues.
- End destructive habits such as drinking, using drugs, overspending, or risky sex.
- Address symptoms such as changes in eating or sleeping habits, anger, anxiety, irritability, or unpleasant feelings.

Good Luck Warrior!

NOTES:

CHAPTER 6:
TRAIN YOUR MIND

"Winners never quit and quitters never win."
—**Ted Turner**
Media Mogul
(Diagnosed with bipolar disorder)

Your mind is your most powerful ally. Your thoughts are the only thing over which you can exert complete control. What you think and believe becomes a reality and rules your life. However, for those of us who have bipolar disorder, it is a paradox that we must use our mind to fight a disease that at times has the power to take control of it.

Learning strategies and techniques to strengthen your mind will improve brain power, increase emotional well-being, decrease stress, and bring happiness and joy to your life.

Here are several powerful mind-strengthening approaches you can deploy to keep from being triggered into a bipolar episode, manage your bipolar disorder more effectively and advance toward making your dreams come true.

Follow the Path with Heart

"Anything is one of a million paths. Therefore, a warrior must always keep in mind that a path is only a path; if he feels that he should not follow it, he must not stay with it under any condition. His decision to keep on that path or to leave it must be free of fear or ambition. He must look at every path closely and deliberately. There is a question that a warrior must ask, mandatorily, Does this path have a heart?

A path without a heart is never enjoyable. On the other hand, a path with heart is easy—it does not make a warrior work at liking it; it makes for a joyful journey—as long as a man follows it, he is one with it."

– Carlos Castaneda

Regarding making decisions in our lives as to what paths to follow and what paths to avoid, the above words of Carlos Castaneda ring true and cannot be refuted. Use your heart as a GPS to guide you in the direction of your dreams. You will know when you are achieving the results you are striving for when your heart leaps for joy. A path with heart is formed by deliberately selecting a number of things that you want to involve yourself with: relationships, vocations, hobbies, arts, anything that connects your heart with the world. The criteria for selection are peace, joy, and strength.

Follow "The Four Agreements"

I highly recommend reading the book *The Four Agreements,* in which bestselling author Miguel Ruiz reveals the source of self-limiting beliefs that rob us of joy and create needless suffering. Based on ancient Toltec wisdom, The Four Agreements offer a powerful code of conduct that can rapidly transform our lives to a new experience of freedom, true happiness, and love.

The Four Agreements are:

1. **Be impeccable with your Word**
2. **Don't take anything personally**
3. **Don't make assumptions**
4. **Always do your best**

Stop the Internal Dialogue

The internal dialogue (self-talk) is the incessant voice in our heads that has been programmed and groomed to focus on our egos ever since we started to think. Our minds constantly focus on our internal dialogue. It programs and shapes our self-concept.

For example, if you believe you are worthy and strong you will live up to that truth. On the other hand, if you criticize yourself and tell yourself you will never get what you want, you won't.

We are own worst enemies due to the habit we have of criticizing and judging ourselves. We criticize ourselves hundreds of times a day without even realizing it.

The voice in your head isn't even real, but it's ruling your life, and it's a tyrant. Once that voice hooks your attention, it makes you do whatever it wants you to do.

> *"We either make ourselves miserable or we make ourselves strong, the amount of work is the same."*
> **-Carlos Castaneda**

Conditioning yourself to stay in a positive mind frame does wonders for your overall mental health. It is in your power. It is your decision to make.

One technique I use daily that is making a positive difference is paying close attention to my thoughts. If I notice I am thinking in a negative way, ruminating over past events, or worrying about what people think of me, I say out loud my keyword "Noise", and change my train of thought to something more productive. My psychiatrist recommended I try this idea and it has served me well in my experience.

Make Love

In his bestselling book *Think and Grow Rich*, Napoleon Hill talks about is the benefits of sex for maintaining good health:

> *"Sex desire is the most powerful of human emotions. For this very reason, the emotion of sex as a therapeutic agency for maintaining good health has no equal.*
>
> *The emotions are states of mind. When the emotion of love begins to mix itself with the emotion of sex, the result is calmness of purpose, poise, accuracy of judgement, and balance. When love, romance, and sex are combined, these three emotions can lift one to the status of a genius."*

Minimize Self-Importance

Self-importance is our greatest enemy. It is the belief that we are more important than everyone else. Exaggerating one's importance is often accompanied by arrogance, conceit, and egotistical behavior. Think about it, our self-importance causes us to be offended by other people, what they say and what they do. This is a huge waste of energy and our precious time. It weakens us.

Self-importance causes us to:

- Feel offended
- Defend our image
- Complain
- Reject ourselves
- Suffer needlessly
- Feel sorry for ourselves
- Think negatively and gossip about ourselves and others

Don't take yourself so seriously. Reducing self-importance frees up energy that can be rechanneled into furthering your goals, reduces negative thought patterns, eliminates needless anger and suffering, and increases happiness.

Running the Bipolar Marathon

Battling bipolar disorder is a lifelong War that can be compared to running a marathon. Marathon runners train, train, train, and then run the race to the best of their ability. Keep these steps in mind for running your personal bipolar marathon:

1. There are good days and bad days, and sometimes you can't tell the difference until you start.
2. Contrary to popular belief, sleep is not overrated—not in the slightest.
3. Don't forget to breathe.
4. Just because it's raining doesn't mean you should cry.
5. Nobody ever said it was easy.
6. Pain is temporary, but pride lasts a lifetime.
7. Create a plan and stick to it. It may not always work, but if you stay focused and relaxed, it will end up just fine.

8. You've got to try no matter what happens. In the end, you'll have bigger regrets from not trying at all.

9. Strength and courage blossom from the seeds of adversity.

10. Sometimes it's the little things that make the biggest difference.

11. Making it to the starting line is usually a lot harder than getting to the finish.

12. Listen to your body and listen to your mind. Make sure you acknowledge when they may be lying to you.

13. You can't change the past, and you won't alter the future. Enjoy your life in the present and always be positive!

14. Smile—it is contagious and increases endorphins. It actually takes more muscles and energy to frown.

15. It is okay to cry.

16. Don't forget to eat. Food can dictate your mood. If you take medication in the morning like I do, it is critical to eat to stabilize your sugar level and brain chemicals.

CHAPTER 7:
TRAIN YOUR BODY

*"God gave me a great body, and it's my duty
to take care of my physical temple."*
—Jean-Claude Van Damme
Famous Actor
(Diagnosed with bipolar disorder)

If you take care of your body, your body will
in turn take care of you. Your mind and body

are a unit; being good to your body benefits your mind. Taking care of your body will help stabilize your moods and maximize your energy for the battles ahead.

> **What you do to exercise your body is important, but what you don't do to your body is more important**.

By avoiding anything that is harmful, you will not obstruct the way your body naturally functions, and in return, your body will take care of you.

Consistent application of the following actions will tune your body and improve your physical and mental health.

It is Crucial to Get Enough Sleep

For those of us who have bipolar disorder it is **CRUCIAL** to get enough sleep. Lack of sleep is one of the strongest triggers of a bipolar episode (Kvarnstorm, 2018). If you are having trouble sleeping, get a sleep aid from your psychiatrist. You can also try taking Melatonin or ZzzQuil if you want to try something over the counter. Meditation and herbal tea may also help.

Stay Away from Sick People at All Costs

After Covid-19, most of us are already hypervigilant about being infected by someone else, however it is still worth mentioning.

I have an extreme phobia of being around people who are sick. If someone around you is sick (coughing, fever, etc.), or tells you they have recently been sick, immediately distance yourself from them, even if you have to make a scene, like moving to a new seat in a movie theater or at church. Just move away. I follow this rule whether I'm in line at the grocery, at the office, visiting my family, or anywhere else. Sometimes sick people will physically infringe on me, like coming into my cubicle at work to talk, attending a meeting I am at, or standing in close proximity to me. At times it seems like this person who is sick wants to get close to me so they can give the illness away. Don't let them infect you, life is way too short to be sick, especially if you could have done something about it. Living with bipolar disorder is hard enough.

I wrote the paragraph above in December 2019, before the advent of the COVID-19 pandemic currently spreading across the globe. Now it is more important than ever to heed this advice. In fact, it could be a matter of life or death. As of May 1st, 2020, there have been 3,300,000 confirmed cases of COVID-19 worldwide, resulting in 235,000 deaths and 1,040,000 recoveries from the epidemic. The United States is the country which has been hit the hardest by COVID-19, with 1,130,000 confirmed cases resulting in 65,253 deaths and 137,000 recoveries. Scientists are scrambling to find a vaccine as the virus continues to wreak havoc around the world.

Drugs and Alcohol

More than 40 percent of us who have bipolar disorder abuse alcohol or drugs (Cerullo, 2007). Often, this is an attempt to self-medicate. If you drink or do drugs, evaluate whether they are keeping you from being your best self. Also be mindful to consider whether you may be overdoing it to mask or numb your emotions. Drugs and alcohol can trigger an episode if you aren't careful, so treat them with respect.

I'm not preaching here. Believe me, I can relate. I used to smoke pot every day if I had a supply. My favorite brand was White Widow. When I was smoking, it was all or nothing. I used to tell myself I was a better man when I was stoned, with more energy and creativity, like Popeye eating spinach. However, after being in a couple of car wrecks because I was stoned out of my mind and realizing that weed was a contributing factor in my bipolar episodes, I admitted to myself that pot was more detrimental than beneficial for me. It wasn't easy to quit - marijuana is a powerful force. For several months after I quit smoking, I had dreams in which I was rolling joints from a large bag of Sinsemilla containing huge, beautiful, moist, aromatic buds and then toking it up. Now that I have quit, I don't have the urge to smoke anymore. I can be around people who are smoking, and I am not tempted. But to be clear, I am highly cognizant that if I get high even once I will be back to smoking every day, like people in AA know if they take one drink, they are going to get drunk, and getting back on the wagon is going to be hell.

For now, this is the approach that is working for me. You will need to figure out what works best for you.

I like this passage found in the book *The Outsider* by Stephen King, which emphasizes the ritual casting-off of bad habits and improving one's mental health:

> *"Holly paused, looking down at her hands. The nails were unpolished, but quite neat; she had quit chewing them, just as she had quit smoking. Broken herself of the habit. She sometimes thought that her pilgrimage to something at least approximating mental stability (if not genuine mental health) had been marked by the ritual casting-off of bad habits. It had been hard to let them go. They were friends."* (King 2018, p. 415).

As an alternative to self-medicating with drugs and alcohol, learn to use bipolar medications to your advantage instead. Bipolar

medications are very powerful pharmaceutical drugs and if used intelligently can work
wonders.

Stay Hydrated

Pay attention to what your body is telling
you - when you feel thirsty, replenish. It is important to flush your system and hydrate. In addition, fluids are very helpful when you are trying to lose weight because it reduces your appetite. Staying hydrated also helps your mind
function more effectively.

Get Fresh Air and Sunshine

Getting fresh air every day clears your head,
calms you, and helps you appreciate the fact that
you are alive on this awesome earth. Soak up
the sun when you can. Looking directly at the
sun with your eyes squinted for a second or two
is a way of gathering energy.

Stretch Your Body Every Day

Stretch your arms, legs, torso, and neck every day. Try to stay supple. This is especially important after sitting for extended periods of time.

Exercise

If you take care of your body, it will take care of you. Take walks, run, ride your bike, lift weights, dance, use the elliptical, do yoga, play basketball—do anything you enjoy that gets the blood pumping.

We are all different physically, and our energy levels vary from person to person. Start at whatever level you are now, and slowly increase your prowess. Build a strong core. In anatomy, the core refers to the body except for the legs and arms. The core is the power center. Besides the physical benefits, a strong core increases your willpower and sharpens your gut instincts.

You may find it easier to accomplish these actions if you incorporate them into your schedule on a consistent basis—for example, take walks every other day during your lunch break.

Get Your Thyroid Checked

Much of our day-to-day well-being—how energetic we feel, how clear our thinking is and how our body processes food is governed by the activity of the butterfly-shaped, thumb-sized thyroid gland at the base of the throat. When it is working as it should, life is good. However, keep in mind that more than 12 percent of the U.S. population will develop a thyroid condition during their lifetime (American Thyroid Association, Appendix A). The good news is that thyroid disease can be managed with medication.

Thyroid disease is associated with bipolar disorder and can actually cause bipolar symptoms as well as diabetes. Anyone who has bipolar disorder should get your thyroid checked. There is a simple blood test that measures the amount of Thyroid Stimulating Hormone

(TSH) in the body. Thyroid medicine can correct either a hypothyroid or hyperthyroid condition, both of which can mimic the symptoms of bipolar disorder.

Note: Taking Lithium every day for a long time can cause thyroid problems as well as impact kidney function. If you take Lithium, then your doctor will have you take blood tests for Lithium levels and kidney functioning on a quarterly basis.

Make an appointment with an endocrinologist and get your thyroid checked out.

NOTES:

INTERLUDE:
THE GREATEST AND THE MOST

Here is a little break from the important stuff. If you always try to live by these ideals, you should be fine:

The most destructive habit **WORRY**
The greatest joy **GIVING**
The greatest loss **LOSS OF SELF-RESPECT**
The most satisfying work
HELPING OTHERS
The ugliest personality trait **SELFISHNESS**

The most endangered species **LEADERS**
Our greatest natural resource **OUR YOUTH**
The Greatest "shot in the arm"
ENCOURAGEMENT
The greatest problem to overcome **FEAR**

The most effective sleeping pill
PEACE OF MIND
The most crippling failure **EXCUSES**
The most powerful force **CREATIVITY**
The most dangerous pariah **A GOSSIP**

AFTER YOUR BIPOLAR DISORDER

The World's most incredible computer	**HUMAN BRAIN**
The worst thing to be without	**HOPE**
The deadliest weapon	**THE TONGUE**
The two most powerful words	**I CAN**
The greatest asset	**FAITH**
The most worthless emotion	**SELF PITY**
The most beautiful attire	**A SMILE**
The most prized possession	**INTEGRITY**
The most powerful channel of communication	**PRAYER**
The most contagious spirit	**ENTHUSIASM**

NOTES:

CHAPTER 8:
RECOVERING FROM A
BIPOLAR EPISODE

"I spent a year in a 12-step program, really committed, because I could not believe what had happened—that I might have killed myself."
—Carrie Fisher
Actress, Screenwriter
(Diagnosed with bipolar disorder)

AFTER YOUR BIPOLAR DISORDER

By definition, a bipolar episode never ends well, unacceptable things have happened, your mind has deceived you, and you crashed and burned. Now you are left to pick up the pieces, regain your balance, and try to get back on an even keel.

This chapter offers tactics and strategies that can speed up your recovery.

Work Closely with your Psychiatrist Regarding Medications

Medication is a big factor that impacts the length of time it takes to recover from a bipolar episode. If the episode was severe, then you may have been heavily medicated with high dosages of strong pharmaceutical medications to bring your symptoms into check. Once your mood stabilizes and your symptoms subside, your psychiatrist will most likely make changes to the medications and/or dosages you are taking. Work closely with your psychiatrist to find the medication cocktail that works best for you.

Have Your Own Space

One thing that was crucial after coming home from the hospital was to have a place I could retreat to and be by myself. This was especially important in the beginning because my mood was still cycling and I felt very shaky, anxious, and at times almost out of control. It took me a couple of weeks until I wanted to be around people more than a short amount of time.

Understand Recovery Takes Time

Recovery does not happen overnight. You should not expect an immediate 100 percent recovery after an episode. As with any illness, there is a period of convalescence. Stability initially means taking things slow. True healing is not just about getting rid of mood swings; it's about letting your brain and body get back on track.

Contact Your Employer

If you are going to miss work because of a bipolar episode, it's important to contact your boss and/or Human Resources as soon as you feel up to it and let them know you won't be coming to work for a few days and will be back as soon as you can. Before you make the call, decide how much you want to divulge. You don't necessarily have to say you are recovering from a bipolar episode but saying you haven't been feeling well and are under a doctor's care can be a valid excuse for missing work. If you are in the hospital, once you feel ready, tell the charge nurse you need to call your boss and they will facilitate the call. Eventually you may have to own up as to why you missed work, but you can cross that bridge down the road. Once you make the phone call, a huge weight will fall off your shoulders and allow you to focus your energy on your recovery.

Monitor Your Moods and Symptoms

While recovering from a bipolar episode it is important to recognize the lingering symptoms you are having due to the illness, as well as the warning signs of a relapse into a manic or depressive episode. If you are having troublesome symptoms or your mood is fluctuating toward mania or depression, make an appointment to see your psychiatrist as soon as you can.

Eliminate Stress

Know your limits, both at home, at work, or at school. Don't take on more than you can handle and make it a priority to make time for you if you are feeling overwhelmed. When you are recovering from an episode, some of the same things that were stressing you out and were instrumental in triggering your episode may still be present. These stressors could be a spouse, boyfriend or girlfriend, roommate, your kids, bills, a sick relative, or other factors.

Use Coping Techniques

Here is a list of coping techniques that can help you recover from a bipolar episode:

- Talk to a supportive person.

- Get a full eight hours of sleep.
- Cut back on your activities.
- Attend a support group.
- Meet with your psychiatrist or therapist.
- Do something fun or creative or write in your journal.
- Take time for yourself to relax and unwind.
- Increase your exposure to light.
- Exercise.
- Eat healthy foods.
- Cut back on sugar.
- Avoid alcohol and drugs.
- Increase or decrease the stimulation in your environment.
- Take adequate breaks of relaxation.
- Take a nature walk.
- Spend time with your loved ones.
- Take a bath or a nap.

Dealing with the People Closest to You

While the things that you do and the way you behave during a bipolar episode vary widely in severity, they are sometimes very disturbing, frightening, threatening, or intolerable. Sometimes sustaining a relationship with a significant other or family member is complicated due to financial insecurity, infidelity, alcoholism, addiction, abusiveness, criminal activity, or other factors that may be associated with the illness.

When your episode ends and you begin the recovery process, do your best to make any amends that need to be made with people who were affected negatively due to your episode. If they seem supportive and want to help, it can be extremely beneficial to include them in your treatment plan. The people in your life want you to get better because they care for you. They also want to protect themselves. They can help you spot symptoms, track behaviors, and gain perspective.

Things People Do That Do Not Aid in Your Recovery

As you can imagine, sometimes you need to set limits with the people you spend time with when you are recovering from a bipolar episode. In most cases they are trying to help you in your recovery but sometimes the things they

do or say are unhelpful. If being around someone is not beneficial to your recovery process,
you might want to put some distance between
you and them. You can always renew your relationship once you are back in control of your
faculties.

Thing's people do that may not help with
your recovery can include:

- Conveying that they are holier than you,
  nagging, preaching, or lecturing.
- Asking how you are doing too frequently.
- Watching and observing you all the time.
- Analyzing and picking apart every thought,
  feeling and action that you have.
- Checking if you are having symptoms too
  often.
- Trying to make you dependent on them.
- Not allowing you to handle situations on
  your own.
- Not respecting your independence.

Attend Bipolar Support Group Meetings

The last thing I wanted to do after being released from the hospital was attend a support

group. But after a few weeks of attending support group meetings, I realized that no matter how I felt before the meetings and no matter what was discussed during them, I always left feeling better.

The wonder of working with a collective is that you get to learn from everyone within it. Often the best lessons came from those who are struggling the most.

This is my personal take about bipolar support groups:

We are comrades in arms waging a mutual fight with the enemy and we've come together to share the horrors of war while shoring one another up for another day of battle.

Here are two organizations which host free support groups around the country:

- Depression and Bipolar Support Alliance (DBSA)

- National Alliance on Mental Illness (NAMI)

These support groups are peer-led which means that the person guiding the meeting knows firsthand what it's like to live with a mood disorder and offer participants an opportunity to share their experiences and gain support from other attendees.

Do an online search to find a bipolar support group in your area.

Forgive Yourself

It makes a big difference if you accept the fact that your bipolar illness is caused by a chemical imbalance in your brain. When you accept you have an actual disease, you can begin to forgive yourself for the bad things that happened during an episode.

> *Accept You Have an Actual Illness*

There is no use in worrying over past events that can't be changed. Have compassion for yourself and focus your energy fully on recovery.

Set Goals for Yourself

Identifying life goals is the essential heart of the recovery process. When we identify and envision a future for ourselves, we begin to become motivated to do all we can to reach those goals.

Remember to break your goals into small steps at first. Ask yourself what you can do now that will help you accomplish your goal. Not only will this help move you closer to your goal, but it will also give you a positive feeling of accomplishment.

Reach out for Face-to-Face Connection

Having a strong support system is essential to staying happy and healthy. Often, simply having someone to talk to face-to-face can be an enormous help in your road to recovery following an episode, as well as boost your outlook and motivation. The people you turn to don't have to be able to "fix" you; they just need to be good listeners.

NOTES:

CHAPTER 9:
PSYCHIATRIC HOSPITALS

"Taking any time off work, acknowledging that I needed to be hospitalized.... I was just so angry. I didn't want to go on the meds. It wasn't until it got bad enough to where I was starting to feel unsafe by myself that I reconsidered."
—**Maria Bramford**
Comedian
(Diagnosed with bipolar disorder)

Bipolar episodes can sometimes end with a stay in a psychiatric hospital, either by voluntarily checking yourself in or being involuntarily committed. Hopefully you will never need to go into the hospital. However, if you do, knowing what to expect is very helpful and can speed up the time it takes for you to recover.

It is an extremely hard decision to check yourself into a psychiatric hospital. However, when bipolar symptoms become severe and you are in the throes of a full-blown manic or depressive episode, checking yourself into the hospital can be the best possible move. Being in a psychiatric hospital is like being in any other hospital: you are there to heal, calm down, and be safe.

If you think you should check into a psychiatric hospital, do it before things go from bad to worse. Sometimes those of us with bipolar disorder need help and asking for it, although difficult, can help you avoid disaster. If you feel you do not have the strength to do it alone, find someone who supports you to take you to the hospital.

Voluntary Check-In

Three ways to check yourself into a psychiatric hospital include:

1. Go directly to a psychiatric hospital and tell them you need to be admitted. Most times, if you say you are suicidal at your evaluation, that's sufficient evidence for immediate admittance.
2. Work with your psychiatrist to be admitted.
3. Go to the emergency room of a hospital and tell them exactly what's going on and what you are thinking. They will transport you to a psychiatric hospital.

Involuntary Commitment

Involuntary commitment is the act of placing someone into a psychiatric hospital or similar facility without their consent. Although this may seem harsh, it is sometimes necessary to prevent people from harming themselves or others and to ensure that appropriate treatment is administered. Involuntary commitment is discussed in more detail in Chapter 10, Legal Rights.

Reasons to Check into a Psychiatric Hospital

- You are having thoughts of hurting yourself or others.
- You are having bizarre or paranoid ideas (delusions) or hallucinations.
- You have not slept or eaten for several days.
- You have serious problems with alcohol or drugs.
- You are thinking or talking too fast, jumping from topic to topic, or not making sense.
- You feel too exhausted or too depressed to get out of bed or take care of yourself or your family.
- You have tried outpatient treatment (therapy, medication, and support) and still have symptoms that interfere with your life.
- You need to make a major change in your treatment or medication under the close supervision of your doctor.

I have been in a psychiatric hospital three times due to bipolar episodes. I voluntarily checked myself in when I had my first episode in 1993 and was involuntarily committed for my second major episode in 2005 and my third major episode in 2015. The following is a list of things I learned along the way.

How Hospitalization Can Help

Hospitalization can help in the following ways:

- The hospital is a safe place where you can begin to get well. It is a place to get away from the stresses that may be worsening your symptoms.
- It's a private way to get help when you need it. You don't have to tell anyone from outside the hospital where you are, even your family, if you choose not to.
- You can work with professionals to stabilize your severe symptoms, keep yourself safe, and learn new ways to cope with your illness.

- You can talk about traumatic experiences and explore your thoughts, ideas, and feelings openly.
- You can learn more about events, people, or situations that may trigger your manic or depressive episodes and how to cope with or avoid them.
- You may find a new treatment or combination of treatments that work.
- You will have time to reflect on your current situation and what improvements you can make.

Useful Tips:

If you find yourself in a psychiatric hospital:

- It is important to go with the flow. Get along with the hospital staff – nurses, doctors, administrators. They want you to get better.
- Stay away from other patients who are acting crazy.
- Contact your employer if you are missing work once you feel up to it.

- You can't leave the hospital until the doctor(s) allow you to, even if you checked yourself into the hospital voluntarily.
- Regroup, rest, regain your energy.
- Don't leave the hospital until you feel ready and have a plan for what to do next.

NOTES:

CHAPTER 10:
LEGAL RIGHTS

"Perilous highs and desperate lows and extravagant flurries of mood are not always symptoms of a broken mind, but signs of a beating heart."
—**Terri Cheney**
Lawyer, Writer
(Diagnosed with bipolar disorder)

If you have bipolar disorder there are certain legal issues that may arise related to your condition, including job discrimination, consent to treatment issues, and trouble with the law. Legal rights for the mentally ill vary by state and by country. Always consult a lawyer who is versed in the laws where you live for legal advice.

Legal ramifications of bipolar disorder include:

- Your legal rights as an employee based upon the Americans with Disabilities Act.
- The laws governing involuntary commitment.
- Your legal rights as a patient in a psychiatric hospital.
- Your legal rights if you are incarcerated.
- Whether you can be forced to take medication.
- The process of getting discharged from a psychiatric hospital.
- The benefits of having a Psychiatric Advance Directive.

Reference Appendix A for websites containing detailed information about legal rights for the mentally ill.

Legal Rights as an Employee

One of the serious repercussions of having bipolar disorder is that you may miss work, sometimes days or even weeks at a time, especially if hospitalization occurs. It is important to know that if you have bipolar disorder, you often have disability rights with your employer and you can take measures to protect your job. This includes many essential benefits, including health insurance. If you find yourself in this situation, talk to Human Resources at your work (discreetly if possible) about your disability rights.

If the worst case happens and you become unemployed, you may still have rights with your employer. Consult a lawyer who specializes in employment law to find out if you have any recourse.

The Americans with Disabilities Act

The Americans with Disabilities Act (ADA) is a law that gives civil rights protection to individuals with disabilities. The ADA's legal definition of a disability is especially beneficial to those with bipolar disorder. According to the US Equal Employment Opportunity Commission, the ADA defines the term disability as "A physical or mental impairment that substantially limits a major life activity." Since bipolar disorder seriously affects people's ability to work, the ADA is of vital importance to those with the disorder. It ensures that people with bipolar disorder have rights at work and, in serious cases, provides them with disability benefits if they are unable to work due to their condition. Note that there are some restrictions that may apply in specific circumstances.

I was employed by different employers during two of my bipolar episodes, both of which involved me being hospitalized in a psychiatric hospital. I was fortunate in both cases. Once I came to my senses, I called my boss from the hospital and told him where I was and that I would get back to work as soon as I could. In each case my supervisor got Human Resources involved and I was thankfully able to keep my job.

To find out more about the ADA, consult Appendix A as well as the following website: https://www.ada.gov/

Legal Rights as a Patient in a Psychiatric Hospital

If you find yourself in a psychiatric hospital you have the following legal rights:

- It is your legal right that the hospital staff verbally explains and provides you with a written copy of the privacy policy, which gives you the right to choose whether you want to have visitors or not. If there are certain people you do not wish to see or hear from, the staff will ask you to write down their names, and they will make a note of it. If you do not wish to have outside friends, family members, employers, or anyone else know you're there, the staff will not make your presence known. They cannot legally verify in any way that you are a patient.
- You may immediately make telephone calls to get help with legal, medical, and mental health issues.
- You have the right to be visited by your clergy, lawyer, or physician at any time.

- You have the right to ask for help from hospital staff to make sure your rights are honored.
- You have the right to a civil commitment hearing, where a judge will decide whether you should be hospitalized by court order. You have the right to a court-appointed attorney at the court hearing. It is highly recommended to have a lawyer represent you at a court hearing to protect your legal rights.
- You have the right to an independent expert evaluation of your mental condition. If you can't afford this evaluation, it must be provided to you at no charge.
- You have the right to file a grievance with the hospital if you feel your rights have been violated. You can request the hospital's clients' rights officer to help you with filing your grievance.
- There is no time limit on an inpatient stay, and you may stay as long as you are willing, and the medical staff believes there is a continued need for inpatient treatment.

- You can't leave the hospital until the doctor(s) allow you to, even if you checked yourself into the hospital voluntarily.
- You may communicate by sealed mail with any individual, group, or agency.
- You have the right to be furnished with writing materials and reasonable postage.
- You have the right to receive mail, unless the head of the hospital determines it is medically harmful for you to receive mail.
- You have the right to receive visitors at regular hours, unless the head of the hospital determines it is medically harmful for you to receive visitors. The people who want to visit you must be notified immediately when you have recovered sufficiently to receive visitors.
- You have the right to wear your own clothes.
- You have the right to keep and use personal possessions (excluding anything deemed potentially harmful), including toilet articles.
- You have the right to request to be released from the hospital.

Legal Rights Regarding Medication Refusal

The standard procedure for dealing with medication refusal is to take the patient to court to legally force him or her to agree to take it. At the trial, the doctor(s) treating you will explain exactly why they think you need to be hospitalized and why it is important for you to take medication. The judge then rules that you either must take medication or don't have to take it. If so, this means that even if you refuse medication, you are legally obligated to take it. When you return to the psychiatric hospital, the doctors will offer you oral meds first, but if you do not take them, staff members will physically restrain you and administer the medication (Mind for better mental health, 2020).

The Benefits of Having a
Psychiatric Advance Directive (PAD)

There is a very simple form called a Psychiatric Advance Directive (PAD) that you can complete in advance of any potential future hospitalizations.

A PAD is a legally binding document that allows you to stipulate treatment, medication and other factors in the event you are hospitalized.

After completing a PAD you need to sign and date along with your trusted person(s). You can change your PAD at any time. A PAD can give you peace of mind and helps ensure you are actively involved in your own recovery.

Consult the National Resource Center on Psychiatric Advance Directives for information and to download a form for creating a PAD.

In addition, Appendix A includes other references regarding PAD's.

To find out more about PAD's, consult Appendix A as well as the following website: www.nrc-pad.org

NOTES:

WINNING THE WAR AGAINST
BIPOLAR DISORDER

*"Make a bipolar battle plan, be a warrior,
and fight the war against bipolar disorder.
Victory means living a productive, happy life,
and making your dreams come true!"*
—Troy Steven, Writer, Aerospace Engineer
(Diagnosed with Bipolar Disorder)

My hope is that by reading this book you have gained the toolset, expertise and proficiency to successfully fight and win the war against bipolar disorder.

Major Takeaways from this Book

The major takeaways from this book include:

> **You must take complete responsibility for managing your illness. No one else is going to do it for us. Live by the motto:**
> ***Bipolar Heal Thyself!***

> **Fighting Bipolar Disorder is Truly a War**

The consensus of the medical community is that successful treatment of Bipolar Disorder depends on diligently following a comprehensive treatment plan, including:

- *Educating yourself about the illness*
- *Medication*
- *Communicating with your psychiatrist and therapist*
- *Having a strong support system*
- *Helping yourself by making healthy lifestyle choices*

Create your personal Bipolar Battle Plan by following the instructions in Chapter 1

Bipolar Battle Plan Toolkit:

Train Yourself to be a Bipolar Warrior

Make the commitment to become a warrior, master the tools in your bipolar battle plan, and win the war against bipolar disorder. Winning the war means never having another out-of-control bipolar episode that causes you to attempt suicide, harm yourself or others, end up in the psychiatric hospital, wreck your finances, lose your job, destroy relationships with friends and loved ones, or destroy your health.

Make the Decision to Win the War against Bipolar Disorder NO MATTER WHAT

VICTORY MEANS LIVING A PRODUCTIVE, HAPPY LIFE— AND MAKING YOUR DREAMS COME TRUE!

If you find this book useful, please take a few moments to write a short review. Your help in spreading the word is highly valued and reviews make it much easier for readers to find the book. Thanks! Troy

https://www.amazon.com/dp/B0BCD5C7BL#customerReviews

CONNECT WITH ME?

Email: troy@breakingbipolar.life
Website: https://breakingbipolar.life/

https://www.facebook.com/troy.ste-ven.7967/

https://twitter.com/life_bipo

https://www.youtube.com/channel/UCh-nUELdoqW_On1DzWoGKqkw

https://www.tiktok.com/foryou

https://www.instagram.com/bipolar_troy/

ALSO AVAILABLE ON AMAZON BY TROY STEVEN

Amazon Link:
https://www.amazon.com/dp/1513650440

APPENDIX A: RESOURCES

- Americans with Disabilities Act (ADA): https://www.ada.gov/
- American Thyroid Association: https://www.thyroid.org/media-main/press-room/#:~:text=More%20than%2012%20percent%20of,are%20una-ware%20of%20their%20condition
- Best Mood Tracker Apps for 2022: https://www.verywellmind.com/best-mood-tracker-apps-of-2021-5212922
- 5 Useful Apps that can assist in the Treatment of Bipolar Disorder: https://interestingengineering.com/5-useful-apps-that-can-assist-in-the-treatment-for-bipolar-disorder https://www.medicalnewstoday.com/articles/324349.php
- bp Magzine. What is bipolar? Summer 2022.
- Caring Info - download and complete your State Advance Directive: https://www.caringinfo.org/planning/advance-directives/by-state/

- Cerullo, Michael. 2007. "The prevalence and significance of substance use disorders in bipolar I and II disorder." Accessed January 6, 2020.
  https://www.ncbi.nlm.nih.gov/pmc/articles/PMC2094705/
- Depression and Bipolar Support Alliance: https://www.dbsalliance.org/support/
- Dome, Peter. 2019. "Suicide Risk in Bipolar Disorder: A Brief Review." Accessed January 6, 2020.
  https://www.ncbi.nlm.nih.gov/pmc/articles/PMC6723289/
- Federman, Russ. 2019, "Bipolar Disorder Without Medication." Accessed July 27, 2022.
  https://www.psychologytoday.com/us/blog/bipolar-you/201910/bipolar-disorder-without-medication
- GoodRx. Prescription Discount Site (huge Savings), Good Alternative to Health Insurance: www.goodrx.com
- Kessler, R. C. 2005. "The Numbers Count: Mental Disorders in America." Accessed March 10, 2013.

https://www.nimh.nih.gov/health/statis-
tics/index.shtml

- Krans, Brian. 2017. "Diagnosis Guide for
  Bipolar Disorder." Accessed September
  25, 2019.
  https://www.healthline.com/health/bipo-
  lar-disorder/bipolar-diagnosis-guide
- Mariant, David. "Surviving Bipolar." Accessed February 14, 2013.
  http://www.survivingbipo-
  lar.com/green_suicide.htm#2
- Mert, Derya. 2013. "Perspectives on reasons of medication nonadherence in psychiatric patients." Accessed September 25,
  2019.
  https://www.ncbi.nlm.nih.gov/pmc/arti-
  cles/PMC4298301/
- Mental Health America - Mental Health
  Rights:
  https://www.mhanational.org/is-
  sues/mental-health-rights
- National Alliance On Mental Health
  (NAMI) Psychiatric Advance Directives
  (PAD):

https://www.nami.org/Advocacy/Policy-Priorities/Improve-Care/Psychiatric-Advance-Directives-(PAD)

- National Institute of Mental Health NIMH:
  http://www.nimh.nih.gov/index.shtml
- Sachs, Gary. 2008. "Are Men or Women More Likely to Develop Bipolar Disorder?" Accessed June 6, 2013.
  http://abcnews.go.com/Health/Bipolar-RiskFactors/story?id=4356077
- Smith, Melinda. 2019. "Depression Symptoms and Warning Signs." Accessed April 4, 2020.
  https://www.helpguide.org/articles/depression/depression-symptoms-and-warning-signs.htm
- The 7 Best Online Bipolar Disorder Support Groups of 2020:
  https://www.verywellmind.com/best-online-bipolar-disorder-support-groups-4802211
- Thompson, Dennis. 2010. "Can Bipolar Lead to Diabetes?" Accessed November 12, 2012.

http://www.everydayhealth.com/bipo-lar-disorder/can-bipolar-disorder-lead-to-diabetes.aspx

- Truschel. 2020. "Bipolar Definition and DSM-5 Diagnostic Criteria." Accessed July 27, 2022. https://www.psycom.net/bipolar-defini-tion-dsm-5/
- Vann, Madeline. 2010. "Are People with Bipolar Disorder Dangerous?" Accessed March 5, 2013. http://www.everydayhealth.com/bipo-lar-disorder/are-people-with-bipolar-disorder-dangerous.aspx
- WebMD. 2019. "Bipolar Disorder and Sleep Problems." Accessed January 7, 2020. https://www.webmd.com/bipolar-disor-der/guide/bipolar-disorder-and-sleep-problems#1

APPENDIX B: GOOD BOOKS & PUBLICATIONS

- BP Magazine: An excellent quarterly magazine about bipolar disorder that also comes in an online version and has a great online forum, making it easy to ask questions and get answers: http://www.bphope.com
- Carlos Castaneda's Don Juan Teachings. Accessed June 6, 2013. http://www.prismagems.com/castaneda/donjuan8.html
- Cheney, Terri. 2009. Manic: A Memoir. William Morrow Paperbacks.
- Fast, Julie. 2012. Loving Someone with Bipolar Disorder: Breaking the Silence about Mental Illness. New Harbinger Publications.
- Napoleon Hill. 1937. Think and Grow Rich. Chartwell Books.
- Hornbacher, Marya. 2008. Madness - A Bipolar Life. New York: First Mariner Books.

- Jamison, Kay. 1996. An Unquiet Mind. New York: First Vintage Books.
- Lund, Sarah Griffith. 2014. Blessed are the Crazy: Breaking the Silence about Mental Illness. Chartwell Books.
- Mikhowitz, David. 2019. The Bipolar Survival Guide: What You and Your Family Need To Know. The Guilford Press.
- Olsteen, Joel. 2011. Everyday is a Friday. FaithWords.
- Ruiz, Miguel. 1997. The Four Agreements. San Rafael: Amber-Allen Publishing. Accessed May 8, 2020. https://www.miguelruiz.com/the-four-agreements
- Steven, Troy. 2020. Breaking Bipolar: - Break the Hold Bipolar Disorder has Over Your Life. Battle Press: http://www.breakingbipolar.life
- Wikipedia is a free online encyclopedia with an excellent overview and description of bipolar disorder: https://en.wikipedia.org/wiki/Wikipedia

Made in United States
North Haven, CT
05 February 2024

48371261R00078